# In the picture

Kevin was looking at one of his car books...

This car book is really good. It's got great pictures in it.

I can draw good pictures of cars, but they take me ages.
The pictures in this car book were taken with a camera, weren't they?
I wish I could take pictures like that.

I think these pictures take ages to do.
Someone makes sure the car is clean, then they put it somewhere that looks good.
Then they take the picture.

Look at this one.
It looks as if it was taken in Africa.
The car is miles from anywhere.
There are lions all around it, but
it's so clean it's gleaming!

Anyway, you could take pictures of cars.
I've got a camera somewhere.
You can use that.

4

I want to take pictures of cars.
Lots of people bring their cars to
Dad's garage for a service or for Dad to mend.
I'll see if there are any good cars at the garage.

I hope there are some good cars in today.

Suddenly, a car screeched to a stop at the pumps.

Wow!

I must get a picture of that!

Kevin stayed at the garage for an hour, but no more good cars came along.

I'm fed up!
I want to take exciting pictures, but there's nothing happening.

You won't get much excitement here. A garage is OK if you want to take a picture of a tyre or an engine or a gear box.

That's no good.
I want exciting pictures of
real things happening!

14

15

You've got a camera!

Yes. I've taken car pictures and I've taken sports pictures. What pictures can I take next?

You could take some animal pictures.

That's a good idea. I could go on safari. Where can I hunt for animals?

20

27

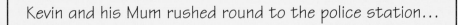

Kevin and his Mum rushed round to the police station...

I didn't know he was in the picture,
but it's him.
It's the car burglar.

If you don't mind,
we'll keep this
for a day or two.
I'll bring it back later.

28

29